Words by Nina Filipek

Illustrated by Jan Smith

Bella is fast asleep in bed.

Every morning her dog,
Max, wakes her up.

What can you see under
Bella's bed?

bed

teddy bear

pillow

clock

hairbrush

comb

curtain
lamp
drawers
ball

mirror
toothbrush
toothpaste
faucet
water
bathtub
soap

Bella's brother, Ben, is in the bathroom.

He's washed his face and now he needs to dry it.

What will he use?

Dad is in the kitchen cooking breakfast.

He will be making Bella some eggs.

What will he use to fry the eggs?

oven mitt
egg
bowl
oven
pan
teapot

The family eats their meals in the dining room.

Mom is setting the table.

What will they use to drink their juice?

plant
apron
spoon
glass
knife
fork
table cloth

Dad opens the garage door.

He is going to drive Bella to the store.

What will Dad drive?

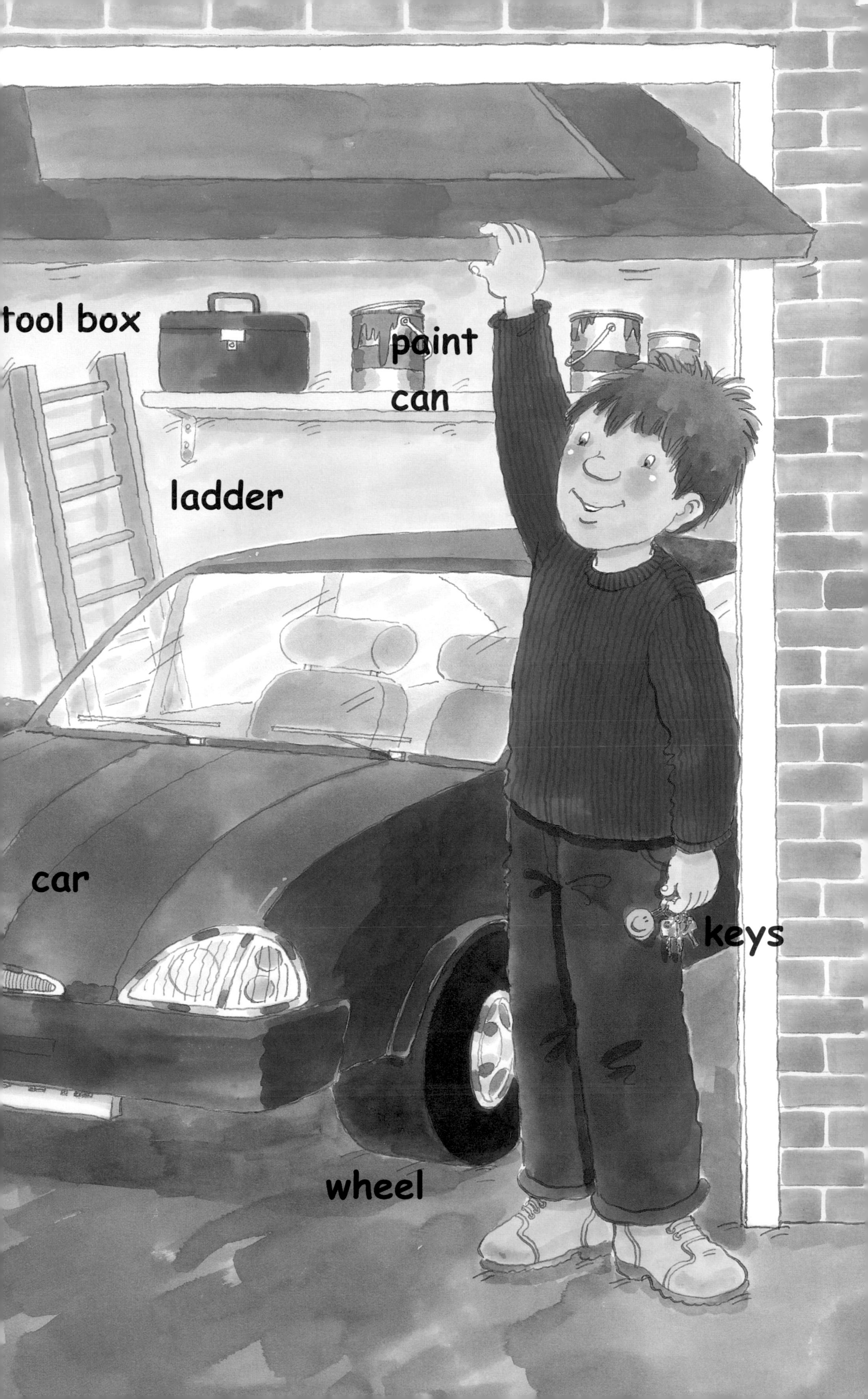
tool box
paint can
ladder
car
keys
wheel

cat
fence
butterfly
pond
fish
bee
flowers
soil
grass

Ben and Max are in the yard.

Max is digging a hole and Ben wants to do some digging, too.

What should Ben use to dig his hole?

Ben and Bella are in the playroom.

It is their special place, where they love to play.

What do Ben and Bella like to read?

blocks
books
paints
truck

light
vase
shelf
fireplace
cushion
chair
rug
television
dog
bone

The family is relaxing in the living room.

It has been a very busy day.

Dad and the children are sitting on the couch.

Where is Mom going to sit?

Ben has fallen asleep
and Bella is very tired.

If you have learned all the
words in this book, you may
be sleepy too!

Goodnight everyone.

photograph
robe
stairs
scarf

The end